"HEROES
OF IRELAND"

IN MYTH & LEGEND

Dáithí Ó hÓgáin

INTRODUCTION

Storytelling in Ireland is a special art and, in this little book, the three most celebrated heroes of these stories are featured. All three have their roots in the Celtic culture of ancient Europe, and it is a tribute to the permanence of tradition in Ireland that they are still household names for many people. Lugh was and is the master of all crafts, Cú Chulainn the athletic hero par excellence, and Fionn the embodiment of wisdom in the human temperament. The imaginations of many generations have played with these characters, and twelve of the most dramatic accounts are selected and retold here.

Dáithí Ó hÓgáin

Iar gcaitheamh an lae más tréith
nó tuirseach mo chnámha,
is go mbraitheann an maor nach éachtach
m'acmhainn ar rámhainn,
labharfad scéal go séimh...

Eoghan Rua Ó Súilleabháin (1748-1784)

When the day is spent
and my bones feel weak and exhausted,
and when the steward notices
that my ability with a spade is not great,
I will gently relate a story...

GUIDE TO PRONUNCIATION

The nearest equivalent in English spelling is indicated in each case. The sound intended by ' kh ' is a fricative ' k ', like the final sound in Scottish ' loch ' or the ' ch ' in German. The stress is normally put on the first syllable of a word :-

BALAR	" boller "
CAOILTE	" kweelta "
CIAN	" keean "
CONALL CEARNACH	" kunnel kaarnokh "
CONCHUBHAR	" kunkhooar ", also " kruhooar "
CORMAC	" kurmock "
CÚ CHULAINN	" koo khullen "
CÚ RAOI	" koo ree "
CULANN	" kullen "
CUMHALL	" kool "
EIMHEAR	" ayver "
EITHNE	" ayhna "
FEAR DIA	" farr deea "
FIANNA	" feeunna "
FIONN	" f-yun ", also " finn " and " f-yoon "
FOMHÓIRE	" fuvoera "
GOIBHNIU	" gwiv-new "
GOLL	" gull ", also " gowl "
LAOGHAIRE	" layra ", also " leera "
LUGH	" looh "
MEADHBH	" mayv "
SÉTANTA	" shaytonta "
TUATHA DÉ	" tooha day "

Tory Island

ULSTER

Navan Fort ●

● Moytirra

C O N N A C H T

River Boyne

L E I N S T E R

Tara ●

M U N S T E R

LUGH

A wonderful people inhabited Ireland long ago. They were called the ' Tuatha Dé ' and were gifted artists and craftsmen. All went well, and life was happy with them for a long time. Then a marauding band of sea-pirates, the Fomhóire, began to attack and harass them. The power of the Fomhóire grew so strong that eventually they controlled all aspects of the life of the Tuatha Dé.

The king of these oppressors was Balar. He was a fearsome warrior, with one eye in his forehead. This eye was full of poison, and it destroyed all on which it gazed. When he looked on a mountainside, the grass and furze was reddened and scorched, and when he looked on a forest all the trees were set ablaze and turned into ashes. He usually kept the eye covered, for its lid was extremely heavy. When going to battle, he set aside four of his soldiers, giving them special instructions to lift that lid. They did so by means of a great polished ring which was attached to it.

Moreover, Balar had a huge fleet of ships, which he kept on the islands off the coast of Ireland, ready to attack and punish anybody who opposed his will.

As a result of the heavy tribute which he collected from Ireland, Balar lived in sumptuous riches on Tory Island off the north-west coast. He had reason to fear nothing, for one of his druids had prophesied that he would never be overthrown except by a grandson. Balar had only one child - a daughter called Eithne - and when she grew up he kept her locked in a tower where she could meet no man. However, a handsome youth of the Tuatha Dé, Cian by name, gained access to her and she became pregnant by him.

When Balar discovered this he was livid with anger. He slew Cian, and had Eithne closely watched. In time she gave birth to a baby boy. Balar gave orders that the infant be killed, but a clever smith called Goibhniu secretly went to the palace and smuggled it away to his forge on the mainland. The little boy grew up in safety there, for Balar believed that he had been put to death . The smith fashioned a mighty spear for him, suitable for a great warrior, and he was the most handsome and intelligent youth in Ireland. His name was Lugh.

The oppression by the Fomhóire became so severe that the Tuatha Dé decided to rebel. When news of this reached Balar, the tyrant assembled his massive fleet and sailed for Ireland in order to reduce the Tuatha Dé to complete slavery. Despairing of their position, the Tuatha Dé assembled at their fortress at Tara to make whatever preparations they could.

The doorman noticed a young stranger approaching, and demanded to know his business. 'I am a wright, and I have come to assist the Tuatha Dé,' the stranger said. The doorman told him that he was not required, as they already had a wright within. The stranger said that he was a builder but was informed that a very skilled builder also was within.The reply was similar when he said that he was a smith, a warrior, a harper, a poet, a physician. The Tuatha Dé already had an expert at each of these trades.

But,' declared Lugh, 'have you one single man who possesses all of the skills together?' Such a one was not to be found in Tara, and so Lugh was allowed to enter.

The king of the Tuatha Dé had lost his arm in combat, and it was not fit that a man with a blemish should command an army. Therefore, Lugh was appointed to lead the Tuatha Dé, in the forthcoming clash with the tyrant's host.

He called together the various chiefs of the Tuatha Dé, and enquired of each of them which skill he possessed. He then made his plan for battle, allotting to all of them their appropriate roles, and began to advise and encourage them.

Battle was joined at Moytirra, and so fierce was it that the warriors, as they hacked at each other, slipped on the blood which flooded the ground. Lugh at first stayed apart from the fighting, but circled around the enemy on one foot, with one eye closed and chanting a magic poem. He then fought his way through the hostile army until he came to where the tyrant leader was.

Balar turned his eye to gaze upon Lugh, but the young hero cast his spear at him and drove the eye to the back of his head. Balar fell down dying, and the venom of his gaze was turned onto his own host. The strength of the Fomhóire drained away, and the Tuatha Dé, with Lugh at their head, made an all-out attack on the foe and gained a great victory.

CÚ CHULAINN

The boy Sétanta was a nephew of the king of Ulster, Conchubhar, who lived at Navan Fort. It so happened that Conchubhar and his nobles were invited to a feast by the rich smith called Culann. This Culann had a ferocious hound which guarded his fortress for him at night. So massive was the hound that three chains were needed to restrain it, with three men holding each chain.

The king forgot to bring the boy with him to the feast. When all the guests were inside his dwelling and the door locked, Culann released the hound. Howling loudly, it circled around the fortress. Then it sat down on a mound, with fiercely staring eyes and bristling neck. Presently the little boy came on the scene, lightheartedly playing with his hurley-stick and ball. The hound attacked him savagely, but the boy struck the ball with his hurley, driving it into the monstrous gullet and choking the hound.

Hearing the commotion, the king and his men rushed from the fortress, and found to their surprise that the hound had been slain by the boy. The smith, however , now had no means of protecting his fortress, and the boy undertook to perform that duty until a new watchdog could be found. Hence his name was changed from Sétanta to Cú Chulainn, which means 'Culann's Hound'.

A curse hung like a shadow over king Conchubhar and his men. The curse had been put on them by a woman whom they illtreated, and according to it, in their hour of greatest need, they would all be struck down with the pains of childbirth and could do nothing to defend themselves.

When the fierce queen Meadhbh of Connacht massed her forces and launched an attack on Ulster, Conchubhar's whole army was smitten by the curse. Cú Chulainn was not an Ulsterman by birth, and thus he was free from the ill effects. Though still a mere youth, he took the field, and each day slew one of Meadhbh's champions in single combat.

Meadhbh knew that the only man who stood a chance against him was a warrior called Fear Dia, who was in her army although he had been trained in Ulster and was a close friend of Cú Chulainn. Fear Dia refused to fight his friend, despite all kinds of cajoling and offers of rich rewards. Then Meadhbh resorted to treachery. 'I understand now,' she said, 'that Cú Chulainn spoke the truth when he said that you were afraid of him !' Stung by this, he agreed to fight.

The two champions fought for three whole days in a river while Meadhbh's army looked on. On the third day, Cú Chulainn cast a javelin from his toes under the water and slew his opponent. Fear Dia died in the arms of the friend turned foe.

Cú Chulainn was so handsome that all the ladies of Ulster were in love with him, and this caused no small upset to the men of the province. King Conchubhar sent messengers throughout Ireland to discover if there was any maiden so accomplished as to be a suitable wife for him. The messengers returned, saying that there was no such one.

But there was, and Cú Chulainn himself set out to the province of Leinster, where a beautiful and wise girl called Eimhear lived. Seeing the handsome but sad-faced young man approach, Eimhear spoke to him in riddles, and he answered in equally mystical language. She told him that he could not have her hand until he performed a number of difficult tasks. He must be able to deliver a single sword-stroke to nine warriors in battle, which would slay them all but the man in the middle. He must also be able to go without sleep from November to August, and he must be able to perform the 'salmon-leap'. This feat involved vaulting from his chariot, somersaulting, and landing on his feet with his weapons ready for combat.

Cú Chulainn was determined to meet her demands. He set out for Scotland, where there were some celebrated schools of arms, and after many perilous adventures there he became the most skilled of all the warriors. When he returned, Eimhear consented to marry him.

Great contention arose in Ulster concerning which warrior of the royal household was the greatest. There were three principal contenders for the honour - Conall Cearnach, Laoghaire, and Cú Chulainn. The Ulstermen could not decide between the three, so they were sent south to Munster to have their courage tested.

There lived in Munster at that time a great champion and wizard called Cú Raoi, and he was asked to choose one of them above the others. Cú Raoi set them the task of guarding his fortress against demons and monsters, and only Cú Chulainn succeeded in warding off the assailants. Cú Raoi therefore ruled in his favour. When they returned home, however, Conall Cearnach and Laoghaire denied that Cú Chulainn had been selected.

The Ulstermen were perplexed, but one night a huge man wielding an axe arrived at their court. He challenged any man present to decapitate him and be decapitated in turn. Several warriors were willing to cut the stranger's head off, and each time that they did so he magically replaced it on his body. Cú Chulainn alone was willing to play the second part of the game. He laid his neck on the block in anticipation of the blow, but the huge man brought down the blunt side of the axe and declared that this warrior was the greatest of all. The stranger was Cú Raoi in disguise, who had come to ensure that his decision was made public.

FIONN

The hero Fionn was the son of the champion named Cumhall. His father was leader of the famous Fianna band of warriors, but he was slain in battle before Fionn was born. Cumhall's rival, Goll, took command of the Fianna, and Fionn was placed by his mother in the care of a nurse and reared in secret for fear of Goll.

When he was seven years old, Fionn left the nurse and set out on his own. Coming to the river Boyne, he met a wise old man there, who had been for years trying to catch a fine salmon which dwelt in that water. The old man caught the salmon and asked Fionn to cook it on a spit for him. As the salmon began to sizzle, a blister rose on it, and the curious boy put his thumb to the blister to burst it. The thumb was burned, and Fionn put it into his mouth to relieve the pain. Immediately he felt a great change coming over him. He could see into the past and the future, and every word he spoke was poetry.

The old man was very disappointed, for this was the salmon of knowledge and the person who got the first taste of it would be a seer. That gift, however, was destined for the fair-haired young hero. Ever after, when Fionn chewed his thumb, anything which he wished to know would be revealed to him.

Through his special knowledge, Fionn realised that the time had come for him to regain his father's command of the Fianna. So he went to the royal fortress of Tara, where the Fianna served the high-king of Ireland.

When he arrived there, it was time to celebrate the feast of November, but he found the royal household much troubled. It was explained to him that each November Eve a phantom came to Tara and set the fortress on fire. No warrior, no matter how great, had managed to prevent this, for the phantom always came playing magical music which put all to sleep.

Fionn offered to confront the phantom, and when night came he sat up outside the fortress waiting for the sinister visitor. He placed his forehead on the point of his spear, so that each time he nodded off to sleep it pricked him and he awoke again. In this way, he succeeded in staying awake despite the weird music, and when the phantom appeared he attacked it and slew it with a spear-cast.

When morning came, all realised that Tara had been saved from the burner. The high-king appointed Fionn leader of the Fianna band, and even Goll was reconciled to the brilliant young son of his enemy.

ne of the leading members of the Fianna band was a great runner called Caoilte. This man had extraordinarily long legs, and so fast was he that his knees used to be bound with a cord so as to allow Fionn and the rest of the warriors to keep pace with him. When running freely Caoilte was a puzzle to onlookers, for he used to raise his shoulders, and so blurred was the speeding image that he appeared to have three heads. He once showed his superb ability by collecting all the hares in Ireland and keeping them overnight in a house at Tara. The house had twelve open doors, and all night long Caoilte raced around it on the outside. He ran so swiftly and so continuously that no hare got the opportunity to escape.

When Ireland was under threat of invasion, the high-king Cormac wished to have a fistful of sand brought to him each morning from every beach in Ireland, for he could tell by examining the sand if a strange foot had passed over it during the night. Caoilte offered to collect the sand, and Cormac asked how long would it take him to do so. 'As long as it takes a woman to change her mind!' said Caoilte. The king was impressed by his answer and directed him to set out on his task. 'I have just returned!' said Caoilte, presenting the sand.

Fionn was a great hunter, and used to chase his quarry for days on end. He went astray in a mist once, and when night fell he was very glad to come upon a little house nestling in a lonely valley.

He entered the house, and was received by an old greybearded man and a beautiful young woman. They invited him to partake of a fine meal, but when he sat down a sturdy young ram rushed up to him and butted the table, upsetting it and knocking over the food and drink. Fionn tried to catch the ram and tie it down, but it butted him too and knocked him on the flat of his back. Then the old man got up and effortlessly tied the ram to the wall.

As the night wore on, Fionn tried to court the beautiful lady, but she rejected him, saying: 'You had me once, and you will never have me again!'

Fionn was amazed, and before he left next morning he remarked to his hosts that he found this a very strange house. Then the old man explained all. 'The ram is the world, full of energy and impetuosity, but I am time, and all must submit to me. The beautiful lady is youth - you had that once, and you will never have it again!'

Fionn praised that house, but he was sad, for he knew that the glory of his youth had gone forever.

MYTHS & LEGENDS OF IRELAND SERIES

KINGS OF IRELAND

QUEENS OF IRELAND

ANIMALS OF IRELAND

HEROES OF IRELAND

REAL IRELAND

© **REAL IRELAND DESIGN LIMITED**
Front Cover Design: Joe Reynolds
Text: Dáithí Ó hÓgáin MA PhD
Layout: Target Marketing Ltd.

HEROES OF IRELAND
IN MYTH AND LEGEND
ISBN 0 946887 06 3